Seventeen solid gold standards.

BACHARACH & DAVID · GOLD CLASSICS

Wise Publications

LONDON / NEW YORK / SYDNEY

Exclusive distributors:
Music Sales Limited
8/9 Frith Street, London W1V 5TZ, England.
Music Sales Pty Limited
120 Rothschild Avenue, Rosebery, NSW 2018, Australia.

This book © Copyright 1989 by Wise Publications
UK ISBN 0.7119.1775.2
Order No. AM 78966

Music Sales' complete catalogue lists thousands of titles and is free from your local music shop, or direct from Music Sales Limited.
Please send a cheque/postal order for £1.50 for postage to: Music Sales Limited, Newmarket Road, Bury St. Edmunds, Suffolk IP33 3YB.

(There's) Always Something There To Remind Me

MUSIC BY BURT BACHARACH • WORDS BY HAL DAVID

Moderate Tempo

I walk a
When sha - dows
If you should

long the cit - y streets you used to walk a - long— with me,—
fall I pass the small ca - fe where we would dance— at night,—
find you miss the sweet and ten - der love we used— to share,—

And ev - 'ry step I take re -
And I can't help re - call - ing
Just come back to the plac - es

love you _____ and I will nev - er be

free. You'll al - ways be a part of me. _____ Wo — wo —

wo. _____   wo. _____

Repeat and Fade

I'll nev - er love an - oth - er, ba - by. __
I nev - er will for - get you, ba - by. __
You'll al - ways be a part of me, oh. __

6

Anyone Who Had A Heart

MUSIC BY BURT BACHARACH · WORDS BY HAL DAVID

take me ____ in his arms and ____ love me

too.   You   could-n't real-ly have a   heart   and

hurt   me ____   like   you   hurt   me   and   be   so   un -

true.   What   am   I   to   do? ___   Ev-'ry   time   you   go   a - way, ____   I   al-ways   say ___

8

this time it's good-bye, dear. Lov-ing you the way I do, ___ I take you back; ___

With - out you I'd die, dear. ___ Know - ing I love you

so. An - y - one who had a heart would

take me ___ in his arms and ___ love me

love me, Why won't you? _____ An-y-one who had a heart would love me

too. _____ An-y-one who had a heart would sure-ly

fade out

take me ___ in his arms and ___ al-ways love me, ___ Why won't

Do You Know The Way To San Jose

MUSIC BY BURT BACHARACH · WORDS BY HAL DAVID

Weeks turn in - to years. How quick they pass, and all the stars
Dreams turn in - to dust and blow a - way, and there you are

that nev - er were are park-ing cars and pump-ing gas.
with-out a friend. You pack your car and ride a - way.

I've got lots of

friends in San Jo - se.

14

Do you know the way to San Jo - se?

Can't wait to get back to San Jo - se.

(Tacet)

Keep repeating and fade

I Say A Little Prayer

MUSIC BY BURT BACHARACH · WORDS BY HAL DAVID

18

you.   Please love me too.

I'm   in love with you.   An - swer my

prayer.   Say you love me too.

I'll Never Fall In Love Again

MUSIC BY BURT BACHARACH • WORDS BY HAL DAVID

What do you get when you fall in love, __ A girl {guy} with a pin to burst __ your bub-ble, That's what you get for all your trou-ble, I'll nev-er fall in love a - gain. __

I'll nev-er fall in love a-gain.

1. What do you get when you kiss a {guy,/girl,} You get e-nough germs to catch
2. What do you get when you give your heart, You get it all bro-ken up
3. What do you get when you need a {guy,/girl,} You get e-nough tears to fill

___ pneu-mo-nia, Aft-er you do, she'll nev-er phone you;
___ and bat-tered, That's what you get, a heart that's shat-tered;
___ an o-cean, That's what you get for your de-vo-tion;

I'll nev-er fall in love a - gain.

I'll never fall in love a - gain._____

Don't tell me what it's all a - bout,___ 'Cause I've been there_ and I'm

glad I'm out;___ Out of those chains, those chains that bind_ you, That is why I'm

opt.

here to re - mind___ you.
here to re - mind you. What do you get when you fall in love,___ You

only get lies and pain and sor - row, So for at least un - til to - mor - row,

I'll nev - er fall in love a - gain,_____

Repeat these 4 bars last time

I'll nev - er fall in love a - gain._____

Nev - er fall in love a - gain._____

ritard   *a tempo*

23

One Less Bell To Answer

MUSIC BY BURT BACHARACH · WORDS BY HAL DAVID

Raindrops Keep Falling On My Head

MUSIC BY BURT BACHARACH • WORDS BY HAL DAVID

head. They keep fall-in' so I just did me some talk-in' to the

sun. And I said I did-n't like the way he got things

done. Sleep-in' on the job. Those rain-drops are fall-in' on my

head. They keep fall-in'! But there's one thing I know

29

The blues__ they send__ to meet__ me won't de-feat__ __ me. It won't be long__ till hap-pi-ness__ steps up__ __ to greet me._____

Rain-drops keep fall-in' on my head, but that does-n't mean my eyes will

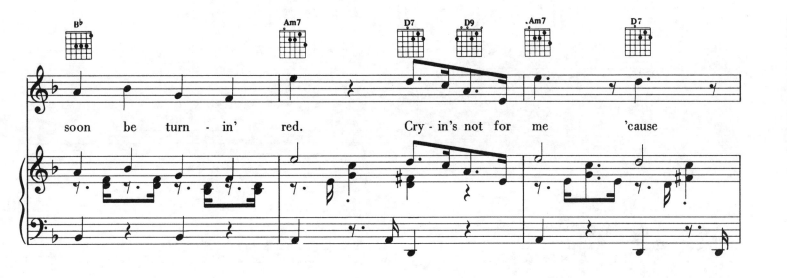

soon be turn - in' red. Cry - in's not for me 'cause

I'm nev - er gon - na stop the rain by com-plain-in'. Be - cause I'm

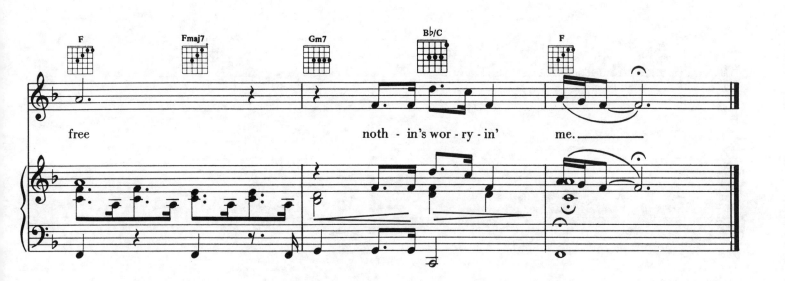

free noth - in's wor - ry - in' me.

This Guy's In Love With You

MUSIC BY BURT BACHARACH · WORDS BY HAL DAVID

You see __ this guy, __ this guy's in love with you. __

__ Yes, I'm __ in love. __ Who

35

Walk On By

MUSIC BY BURT BACHARACH · WORDS BY HAL DAVID

1. If you see me walk-in' down the street   and I start to cry___   each time we meet,
2. I just can't get o-ver los-in' you   and so if I seem___   bro-ken and blue,___

Walk on by,___   Walk on by.___

Make be-lieve___   that you don't see the tears.   Just   let me   grieve___   in
Fool-ish   pride,___   that's all that I have left.   So   let me   hide___   the

pri - vate,   'Cause each time   I   see you,   I break down and cry.
tears and   the sad - ness   you   gave me   when you said good - bye.

Walk on   by,___   Don't   stop,   Walk on   by.___

Don't   stop,   Walk on   by.___

Wishin' And Hopin'

MUSIC BY BURT BACHARACH • WORDS BY HAL DAVID

'cause___ you won't get him think-in' and pray-in', ___ wish-in' and a-hop-in'. ___ 'Cause wish-in' and hop-in' and think-in' and pray-in', plan-nin' and dream-in' his kiss-es will start, ___ that won't get you in-to his heart. ___ So if you're

You'll Never Get To Heaven (If You Break My Heart)

MUSIC BY BURT BACHARACH • WORDS BY HAL DAVID

Moth-er told me al-ways to fol-low the gold-en rule,
I've been hear-ing ru-mors a-bout how you play a-roun';
I can hard-ly wait for the day when we say I do.

And she said it's real-ly a sin to be mean and cruel.
Though I don't be-lieve what I hear, still it gets me down.
It's a day I've dreamed of so long, now it's com-ing true.

So re-mem-ber if you're un-true,— an-gels up in heav-en are
If you ev-er should say good-bye— it would be so aw-ful the
You will prom-ise to cher-ish me.— If you break your prom-ise the

looking_____ at you. _____You'll
angels_____ would cry. _____You'll nev-er get to heav-en if you break my heart.__
angels_____ will see. _____You'll

So be ver-y care-ful not__ to make us part. You won't get to heav-en if you__

1., 2.

break my__ heart, __ Oh no.

3.

no. __

Repeat and Fade

43

Don't Make Me Over

MUSIC BY BURT BACHARACH • WORDS BY HAL DAVID

Slow Rock Tempo

Don't make me o - ver, _____ Now that I'd do an - y - thing

for you. Don't make me o - ver, _____ Now that you know how I a -

dore you. Don't pick on the things I say, _____ The things I do. _____ Just love me with

45

Ac - cept me for the things I __ do. __ Ac - cept me for what I __ am, ____

Ac - cept me for the things I __ do. ____

Repeat and fade

Ac - cept me for what I __ am, ____ Ac - cept me for the things I _ do. __

47

Message To Michael

MUSIC BY BURT BACHARACH • WORDS BY HAL DAVID

fame   fell   through,   to   me {he / she}   will   al -   ways

be   a   star.___   Spread   your   wings   for   New   Or -   leans _____   Ken-tuck- y

Blue -   bird,   fly   a - way _____   and   take   a

mes-sage   to {Mi - chael, / Mar - tha,}   mes-sage   to {Mi - chael. / Mar - tha.}   Ask {him / her}   to

I Just Don't Know What To Do With Myself

MUSIC BY BURT BACHARACH · WORDS BY HAL DAVID

What The World Needs Now Is Love

MUSIC BY BURT BACHARACH • WORDS BY HAL DAVID

With A Jazz Waltz Feel

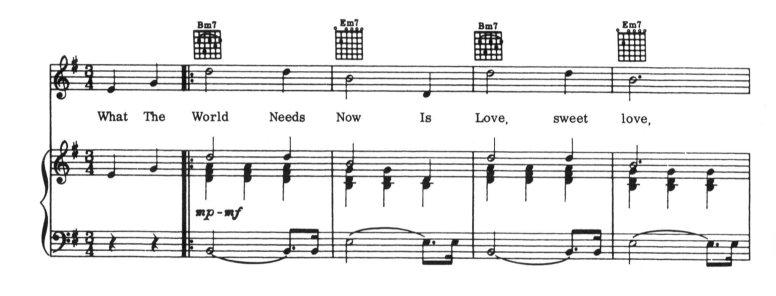

What The World Needs Now Is Love, sweet love,

It's the on-ly thing____ that there's just____ too lit-tle of. What The

World Needs Now Is Love, sweet love,

No, not just for some,_____ but for ev - 'ry - one._____

To Coda ⊕

Lord, we don't need an - oth - er moun - tain,_____ There are
Lord, we don't need an - oth - er mead - ow,_____ There are

57

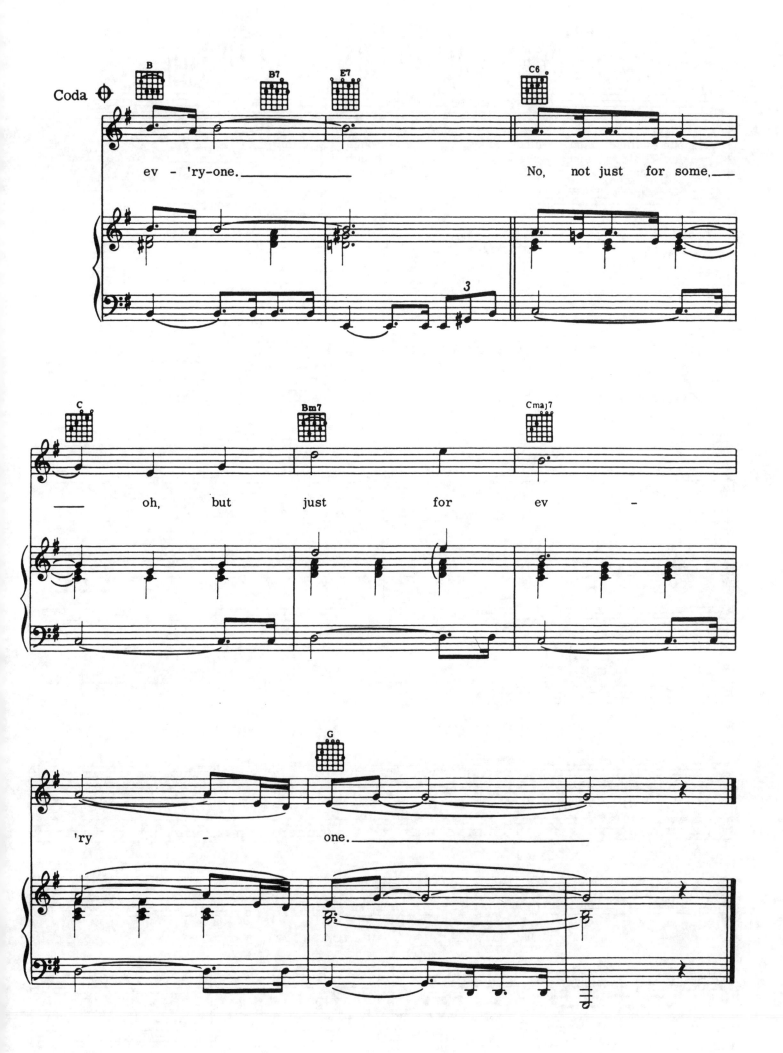

Coda

ev - 'ry-one._____ No, not just for some,___

oh, but just for ev -

'ry - one._____

(They Long To Be) Close To You

MUSIC BY BURT BACHARACH · WORDS BY HAL DAVID

Odds And Ends (Of A Beautiful Love Affair)

MUSIC BY BURT BACHARACH · WORDS BY HAL DAVID

Moderately - not too fast

Your pil-low was-n't slept up - on, your clos-et was emp-ty
could have said good - bye. You should-n't have run a -

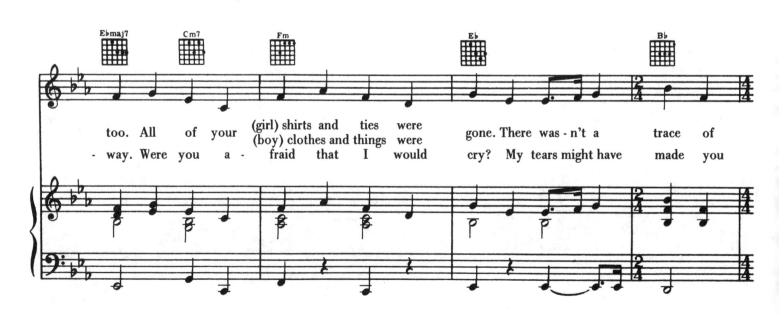

too. All of your (girl) shirts and ties were gone. There was-n't a trace of
(boy) clothes and things were
- way. Were you a - fraid that I would cry? My tears might have made you

How could you go and leave so com-plete-ly?
Gone are the dreams that kept us to-geth - er.

Noth - ing was left of all the mem - 'ries that _____ we used to share._____
Noth - ing is left to show that we were once _____ so hap - py there._____

Just an emp - ty tube of tooth - paste and ___ a half - filled cup ___ of cof -

Printed and bound in Great Britain by
Caligraving Limited Thetford Norfolk

2/06 (57839)